THE DR. NOW 1200-CALORIE DIET PLAN

BEGIN YOUR TRANSFORMATION JOURNEY WITH DR. NOW-ZARADAN'S DIET PROVEN FORMULA FOR WEIGHT LOSS | 365 DAYS OF AFFORDABLE RECIPES

ALICE JOHNSON

TABLE OF CONTENTS

MAIN DISHES

DESSERTS

60-DAY MEAL PLAN

INTRODUCTION

Hello and congratulations on taking the first step towards a healthier, more vibrant you! This book is inspired by the teachings of Dr. Younan Nowzaradan, affectionately known as Dr. Now. He is a renowned surgeon and weight loss expert whose approach has helped thousands of people achieve significant weight loss. This cookbook is designed to help you understand and implement his effective diet strategy through delicious, easy-to-prepare recipes.

Understanding Dr. Now's Philosophy

Dr. Now's dietary approach is centered around the concept of calorie control, balanced nutrition, and realistic changes to eating habits. His methods are not just about losing weight quickly; they focus on making sustainable lifestyle changes that foster long-term health and weight management. The recipes in this book are crafted to align with these principles, offering balanced meals that control calorie intake without sacrificing flavor.

The Power of Eating Right

Obesity is a growing concern in America, and it can lead to various health issues such as diabetes, heart disease, and high blood pressure. By choosing to follow the diet outlined in this book, you're not just aiming to lose weight; you're setting the stage for a healthier life. The recipes here are designed to fill you up with the right nutrients that boost energy and improve overall health.

To maximize your success, each recipe includes detailed nutritional information to help you keep track of what you're eating. The book is divided into sections for breakfast, starters, main dishes, and desserts, making it easy to plan your meals and stick to your goals.

Also included is a 28-day meal plan at the end of the book which takes the guesswork out of what to eat every day.

Understanding Dr. Now's Philosophy

Dr. Younan Nowzaradan, widely known for his effective and compassionate approach to weight loss, believes in a no-nonsense methodology that addresses both the physiological and psychological aspects of eating and health. His philosophy is straightforward yet deeply impactful, focusing on three core principles: calorie reduction, balanced nutrition, and sustainable lifestyle changes.

Calorie Reduction

One of the pillars of Dr. Now's approach is calorie reduction. The goal is to consume fewer calories than you burn, which is essential for weight loss. However, Dr. Now emphasizes that this reduction should not come at the expense of nutritional value. The recipes in this cookbook are designed to be low in calories but high in nutrients, ensuring that every meal contributes to your body's needs without excess calorie intake.

Balanced Nutrition

Balanced nutrition is crucial for overall health and effective weight loss. Dr. Now advocates for a diet that includes a healthy balance of proteins, fats, and carbohydrates. His approach avoids extreme restrictions of any one food group which can lead to unsustainable dieting and potential nutritional deficiencies. Instead, the recipes provided here ensure a well-rounded diet that supports body functions and maintains satiety, helping you to stick to your eating plan more easily.

Sustainable Lifestyle Changes

Perhaps the most significant aspect of Dr. Now's philosophy is the focus on sustainable lifestyle changes. Weight loss is not just about dieting for a few months; it's about adopting a healthier lifestyle for the long term. This cookbook encourages you to learn new eating habits, understand portion control, and incorporate meals that you can enjoy making and eating for years to come. It's not just about losing weight—it's about learning how to maintain a healthy weight.

Mindful Eating and Portion Control

Mindful eating is another key component of Dr. Now's teachings. This involves paying attention to what you eat, savoring each bite, and stopping when you feel full. Portion control is also emphasized to avoid overeating. Each recipe in this book includes serving sizes to help guide you on how much to eat at each meal, which is vital for controlling calorie intake.

Adapting to Individual Needs

Dr. Now understands that each person's body is different, and what works for one might not work for another. Therefore, this cookbook includes a variety of recipes to cater to different tastes and dietary needs, including options for those who are vegetarian, vegan, or need gluten-free meals. The idea is to make the diet as adaptable and enjoyable as possible which is essential for long-term adherence.

The Power of Eating Right

Embracing a healthy diet is more than just a tool for weight loss—it's a fundamental part of improving your overall health and well-being. Dr. Now's diet philosophy extends beyond the simple mechanics of calorie counting. It encompasses a holistic view of nutrition that benefits all aspects of your health, including mental clarity, energy levels, and systemic health.

Enhanced Physical Health

The primary benefit of eating right, as outlined in Dr. Now's teachings, is the positive impact on your physical health. Obesity and poor diet are linked with numerous health problems, including diabetes, heart disease, high blood pressure, and joint problems. By following the recipes in this cookbook, which are rich in nutrients and low in unhealthy fats and excessive sugars, you can help mitigate these risks. Nutritious meals improve cardiovascular health, stabiliz blood sugar levels, and reduce inflammation, all of whic are crucial for a long and healthy life.

Boosted Energy Levels

A well-balanced diet fuels the body efficiently. Many people experience a significant boost in energy when they switc from a diet high in processed foods to one that includes whole, nutrient-dense foods. Each recipe in this cookbook is designed to provide a balanced mix of macronutrients—carbohydrates, proteins, and fats—to sustain your energy throughout the day. This can lead to better physical performance, whether it's during daily activities or exercise, enhancing your ability to burn calories and maintain physical fitness.

Improved Mental Health

Diet also has a profound effect on mental health. Nutritional psychiatry is an emerging field that points to the connection between what you eat and how you feel. Foods rich in vitamins, minerals, and antioxidants can reduce the symptoms of depression and anxiety and elevate mood. The meal plans in this book include ingredients known for their positive effects on brain health, such as omega-3 fatty acids, found in fish and seeds, and magnesium, present in leafy greens and nuts.

Sustainable Weight Management

The ultimate goal of eating right, as promoted by Dr. Now, is not just to lose weight but to maintain a healthy weight long-term. Crash diets can lead to quick weight loss but are notoriously difficult to maintain, often resulting in regaining the weight. The approach here encourages gradual and steady weight loss that results from consistent healthy eating habits. This method is more likely to lead to permanent weight loss and avoids the yo-yo dieting cycle that can be so frustrating and detrimental to your health.

Creating a Positive Relationship with Food

Dr. Now's approach also focuses on developing a healthy relationship with food, which is essential for lasting weight loss. This includes understanding hunger cues, respecting fullness, and enjoying the flavors and textures of food. Learning to see food as nourishment rather than a source of guilt or anxiety can transform your eating habits and your life.

Breakfast

Ingredients

- 3 egg whites
- 1 cup fresh spinach, chopped
- 1/4 cup diced onions
- 1/4 cup diced bell peppers
- Salt and pepper to taste
- Non-stick cooking spray

EGG WHITE SPINACH OMELET

Servings: 1

Prep Time: 5 Mins

Cook Time: 5 mins

Description:

A high-protein, low-calorie omelet packed with spinach for a fiber-rich start to the day.

Preparation steps:

1. Heat a non-stick skillet over medium heat and spray with cooking spray.
2. Sauté onions and bell peppers until soft, about 3 minutes.
3. Add spinach and cook until wilted, approximately 1 minute.
4. Pour the egg whites over the vegetables, season with salt and pepper, and cook until the eggs are set, about 2 minutes. Flip and cook the other side for 1 minute.
5. Serve hot.

GREEK YOGURT & BERRY PARFAIT

Servings: 1
Prep Time: 10 mins
Cook Time: 5 mins

Description:

A refreshing and creamy parfait with layers of yogurt, berries, and nuts, perfect for a no-cook, low-fat breakfast.

Ingredients

- 1 cup non-fat Greek yogurt
- 1/2 cup mixed berries (strawberries, blueberries, raspberries)
- 2 tbsp. granola
- 1 tbsp. honey or to taste
- 1 tbsp. chopped nuts (optional)

Preparation steps:

1. In a glass or bowl, layer half the Greek yogurt.
2. Add half the mixed berries over the yogurt.
3. Sprinkle a tbsp. of granola and half the chopped nuts if using.
4. Repeat the layers with the remaining yogurt, berries, granola, and nuts.
5. Drizzle with honey and serve immediately or chill until ready to eat.

- 1 cup almond flour
- 2 large eggs
- 1/3 cup water
- 2 tbsp. olive oil
- 1 tsp. baking powder
- 1/4 tsp. salt
- Non-stick cooking spray

LOW-CARB PANCAKES

Servings: 2

Prep Time: 10 Mins

Cook Time: 10 mins

Description:

Fluffy and satisfying pancakes made with almond flour for a low-carb, filling breakfast.

Preparation steps:

1. In a mixing bowl, whisk together almond flour, baking powder, and salt.
2. In another bowl, beat the eggs with water and olive oil until smooth.
3. Combine the wet ingredients with the dry ingredients and stir until a batter forms.
4. Heat a skillet over medium heat and spray with cooking spray.
5. Pour 1/4 cup of batter for each pancake, cooking until bubbles form on the surface, then flip and cook until golden brown on the other side, about 2 minutes per side.
6. Serve with sugar-free syrup or fresh berries.

TURKEY AND SPINACH SCRAMBLE

Servings:
2

Prep Time:
5 mins

Cook Time:
5 mins

Description:

Lean ground turkey and spinach make this scramble a nutritious, protein-rich meal to start your day.

Ingredients

- 1/2 pound ground turkey
- 1 cup fresh spinach, chopped
- 2 large eggs
- Salt and pepper to taste
- 1 tbsp. olive oil

Preparation steps:

1. Heat olive oil in a skillet over medium heat.
2. Add ground turkey and cook until browned, breaking it up as it cooks, about 5 minutes.
3. Stir in the chopped spinach and cook until wilted, about 2 minutes.
4. Beat the eggs with salt and pepper, then pour them into the skillet with the turkey and spinach.
5. Cook, stirring frequently, until the eggs are fully set, about 3 minutes.
6. Serve warm.

Ingredients

- 1/4 cup ground flaxseed
- 1/4 cup almond flour
- 1 cup unsweetened almond milk
- 1 tsp. cinnamon
- 1 tbsp. sugar-free sweetener or to taste
- Optional toppings: chopped nuts, berries, or a dollop of Greek

ALMOND & FLAXSEED PORRIDGE

Servings: 2

Prep Time: 5 Mins

Cook Time: 10 mins

Description:

A warm, comforting porridge rich in omega-3 fatty acids and fiber, perfect for a filling low-carb start to your day.

Preparation steps:

1. In a small pot, combine the flaxseed, almond flour, and cinnamon.
2. Add the almond milk and stir well to combine.
3. Heat over medium heat, stirring frequently until the mixture thickens and begins to bubble about 5-7 minutes.
4. Remove from heat and stir in the sweetener.
5. Serve hot, topped with your choice of nuts berries, or Greek yogurt for added flavor and texture.

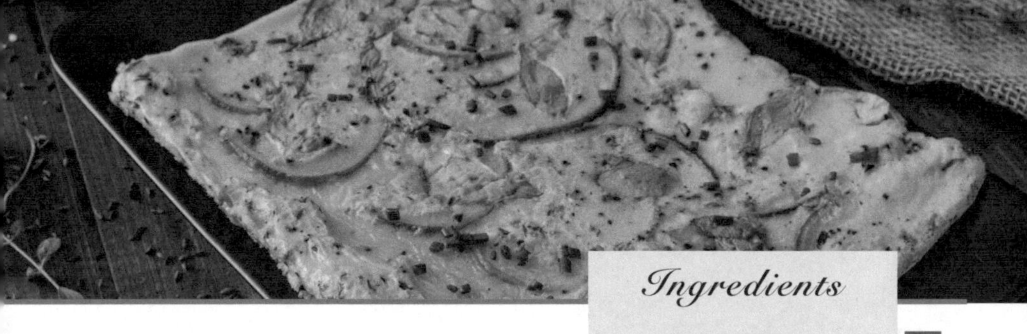

LOW-CARB CASSEROLE

Servings: 2

Prep Time: 15 mins

Cook Time: 35 mins

Description:

This hearty casserole combines eggs, low-fat cheese, and vegetables for a delicious, make-ahead breakfast option.

Ingredients

- 6 large eggs
- 1/2 cup low-fat milk
- 1 cup chopped broccoli
- 1/2 cup diced bell peppers
- 1/2 cup shredded low-fat cheese
- 1/2 tsp. salt
- 1/4 tsp. black pepper
- Non-stick cooking spray

Breakfast

Preparation steps:

1. Preheat the oven to 350°F (175°C).
2. In a large bowl, whisk together eggs, milk, salt, and pepper.
3. Stir in the broccoli, bell peppers, and cheese.
4. Spray a baking dish with non-stick cooking spray and pour the egg mixture into the dish.
5. Bake in the preheated oven until the eggs are set and the top is lightly golden, about 35 minutes.
6. Let cool slightly before serving, or prepare in advance and reheat for a quick and easy breakfast.

Breakfast

Ingredients

- 4 slices turkey bacon
- 2 low-carb tortillas
- 1 ripe avocado, sliced
- 1/4 cup shredded lettuce
- 2 tbsp. low-fat ranch dressing

TURKEY BACON & AVOCADO WRAP

Servings:
2

Prep Time:
10 Mins

Cook Time:
5 mins

Description:
A protein-packed wrap featuring turkey bacon and creamy avocado, ideal for a quick nutritious start to your day.

Preparation steps:

1. Cook the turkey bacon in a skillet over medium heat until crispy, about 5 minutes; set aside.
2. Lay out the tortillas and evenly distribute the sliced avocado, shredded lettuce, and crispy bacon on each.
3. Drizzle with low-fat ranch dressing.
4. Roll up the tortillas tightly, cut in half, and serve immediately for a fresh, satisfying breakfast.

Breakfast

BERRY SMOOTHIE BOWL

Servings: 2

Prep Time: 5 mins

Cook Time: 5 mins

Description:

A vibrant, nutrient-packed smoothie bowl topped with fresh fruits and seeds, perfect for a light yet filling breakfast.

Ingredients

- 1 cup frozen mixed berries
- 1/2 banana
- 1/2 cup unsweetened almond milk
- 1 tbsp. chia seeds
- 1 tbsp. flaxseeds
- Optional toppings: sliced banana, fresh berries, a sprinkle of granola

Preparation steps:

1. In a blender, combine the frozen berries, banana, and almond milk; blend until smooth.
2. Pour the smoothie into a bowl.
3. Top with chia seeds, flaxseeds, and additional banana slices and fresh berries if desired.
4. Serve immediately, enjoying the creamy texture and burst of berry flavors.

Breakfast

Ingredients

- 2 large eggs, beaten
- 1 cup fresh spinach, chopped
- 1/4 cup crumbled feta cheese
- 2 whole wheat tortillas
- Salt and pepper to taste
- 1 tbsp. olive oil

SPINACH AND FETA WRAP

Servings: 2

Prep Time: 10 Mins

Cook Time: 5 mins

Description:

A Mediterranean wrap filled with nutritiou spinach, protein-rich eggs, and tangy fet great for a savory breakfast on-the-go.

Preparation steps:

1. Heat the olive oil in a skillet over medium heat.
2. Add the chopped spinach and sauté until wilted about 2 minutes.
3. Pour the beaten eggs over the spinach, season with salt and pepper, and scramble together until the eggs are cooked through, about 3 minutes.
4. Stir in the feta cheese just until melted.
5. Divide the mixture between the two tortillas roll them up, and serve warm.

COCONUT & MANGO CHIA PUDDING

Servings: 2
Prep Time: 15 mins
Cook Time: 5 mins

Description:
A tropical, make-ahead meal with chia seeds soaked in coconut milk, topped with mango for a delightful start to the day.

Ingredients

- 1/4 cup chia seeds
- 1 cup coconut milk
- 1 tbsp. honey or to taste
- 1/2 mango, diced
- Optional: a sprinkle of shredded coconut for extra flavor

Breakfast

Preparation steps:

1. In a bowl, mix the chia seeds and coconut milk.
2. Sweeten with honey and stir well.
3. Cover the bowl and refrigerate overnight until the chia seeds have absorbed the coconut milk and the pudding has thickened.
4. In the morning, stir the pudding to smooth out any lumps, then top with diced mango and optional shredded coconut.
5. Serve chilled for a refreshing and satisfying breakfast.

Breakfast

- 1 cup steel-cut oats
- 2 cups water or low-sodium vegetable broth
- 1 cup sliced mushrooms
- 1/2 cup diced onions
- 1 garlic clove, minced
- 1 tsp. dried thyme
- 1 tbsp. olive oil
- Salt and pepper to taste

MUSHROOM STEEL-CUT OATS

Servings: 2

Prep Time: 5 Mins

Cook Time: 20 mins

Description:

A savory traditional oatmeal, featuring ste el-cut oats with mushrooms and herbs for hearty, fiber-rich breakfast.

Preparation steps:

1. In a medium saucepan, bring water or broth to a boil. Add steel-cut oats and simmer for 20 minutes, stirring occasionally, until oats are tender.
2. While oats cook, heat olive oil in a skillet over medium heat. Add onions and garlic, sautéing until onions are translucent.
3. Add mushrooms and thyme to the skillet cooking until mushrooms are golden and tender
4. Once oats are cooked, stir in the sautéed mushroom mixture. Season with salt and pepper
5. Serve warm, offering a satisfying, nutrient-dense meal to start your day.

ZUCCHINI & BELL PEPPER FRITTATA

Servings: 4

Prep Time: 10 mins

Cook Time: 20 mins

Description:

Packed with vegetables and eggs, this colorful frittata makes a filling and nutritious breakfast that's perfect for sharing.

Ingredients

- 6 large eggs
- 1 zucchini, thinly sliced
- 1 red bell pepper, diced
- 1/2 onion, diced
- 1/4 cup milk
- 1/4 cup shredded low-fat cheese
- 1 tbsp. olive oil
- Salt and pepper to taste

Breakfast

Preparation steps:

1. Preheat the oven to 375°F (190°C).
2. In a large oven-proof skillet, heat olive oil over medium heat. Sauté onion, bell pepper, and zucchini until soft, about 5 minutes.
3. In a bowl, whisk together eggs, milk, salt, and pepper.
4. Pour the egg mixture over the vegetables in the skillet. Sprinkle with cheese.
5. Cook on the stove for about 5 minutes until the edges begin to set.
6. Transfer the skillet to the oven and bake for 15 minutes or until the center is set.
7. Serve warm, cut into wedges.

Breakfast

Ingredients

- 1 cup non-fat Greek yogurt
- 1 apple, diced
- 1/2 tsp. cinnamon
- 1 tbsp. chopped walnuts
- 1 tsp. honey

CINNAMON APPLE YOGURT BOWL

Servings: 1

Prep Time: 5 Mins

Cook Time: 5 mins

Description:

A satisfying bowl of Greek yogurt mixe with cinnamon-spiced apples, ideal for quick and healthy breakfast.

Preparation steps:

1. In a bowl, mix the diced apple with cinnamon and honey.
2. Layer the spiced apples over the Greek yogurt.
3. Top with chopped walnuts for a bit of crunch.
4. Stir to combine just before eating, enjoying the fresh and creamy flavors.

Breakfast

SMOKED SALMON & CREAM BAGEL

Servings: 1

Prep Time: 5 mins

Cook Time: 5 mins

Ingredients

- 1 whole-grain bagel, halved and toasted
- 2 tbsp. light cream cheese
- 2 ounces smoked salmon
- A few slices of red onion
- Capers (optional)

Description:

A luxurious yet healthy breakfast option, a bagel with smoked salmon and light cream, packed with protein and omega-3s.

Preparation steps:

1. Spread each half of the toasted bagel with light cream cheese.
2. Layer on the smoked salmon, red onion, and capers if using.
3. Serve immediately, enjoying a mix of textures and flavors that are sure to satisfy your morning appetite.

Breakfast

Ingredients

- 2 cups rolled oats
- 1 cup fresh or frozen blueberries
- 1/2 cup unsweetened applesauce
- 1/4 cup honey
- 1 tsp. vanilla extract
- 1/2 tsp. cinnamon
- 1/4 tsp. salt

BLUEBERRY OATMEAL BARS

Servings: 8

Prep Time: 10 Mins

Cook Time: 25 mins

Description:
Bars loaded with blueberries which provid a great source of fiber and antioxidants, per fect grab-and-go breakfast.

Preparation steps:

1. Preheat your oven to 350°F (175°C) and line an 8-inch square baking dish with parchment paper.
2. In a large bowl, mix together the oats, cinnamon, and salt.
3. Stir in the applesauce, honey, and vanilla extract until well combined.
4. Gently fold in the blueberries.
5. Press the mixture evenly into the prepared baking dish.
6. Bake for 25 minutes or until the edges are golden brown and the bars are set.
7. Let cool completely in the dish before cutting into bars and serving.

AVOCADO TOAST & POACHED EGG

Servings: 1

Prep Time: 10 mins

Cook Time: 10 mins

Ingredients

- 1 slice of whole-grain bread
- 1/2 ripe avocado
- 1 egg
- Salt and pepper to taste
- Optional toppings: red pepper flakes, chia seeds

Breakfast

Description:

Avocado spread on whole-grain toast, topped with a perfectly poached egg, makes for a balanced breakfast.

Preparation steps:

1. Bring a pot of water to a gentle simmer.
2. Crack the egg into a cup and gently pour it into the simmering water. Cook for about 4 minutes for a soft poached egg.
3. While the egg is cooking, toast the bread and mash the avocado onto the toast.
4. Once the egg is cooked, use a slotted spoon to remove it from the water and drain it slightly on a kitchen towel.
5. Place the poached egg on the avocado toast. Season with salt, pepper, and optional toppings.
6. Serve immediately for a warm, nutritious start to your day.

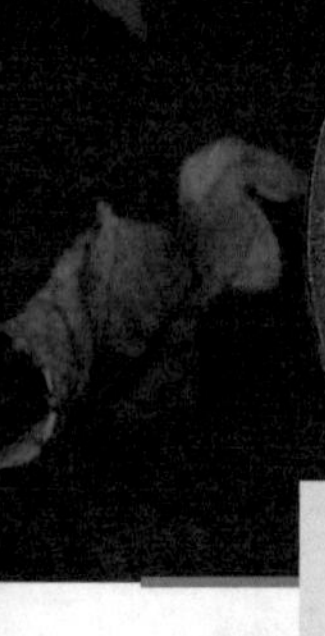

Breakfast

Ingredients

- 2 cups chopped kale
- 4 eggs
- 2 cloves garlic, minced
- 1 tbsp. olive oil
- Salt and pepper to taste

KALE & EGG BREAKFAST SAUTE

Servings: 2

Prep Time: 5 Mins

Cook Time: 10 mins

Description:

A quick sauté of kale and eggs, offering iron, vitamin K, and protein, ideal for kick-starting your metabolism in the morning.

Preparation steps:

1. Heat the olive oil in a large skillet over medium heat.
2. Add the minced garlic and sauté until fragrant, about 1 minute.
3. Add the kale and cook until it begins to wilt, about 3-4 minutes.
4. Crack the eggs directly into the skillet over the kale. Season with salt and pepper.
5. Cover and cook until the eggs are cooked to your desired doneness, about 5 minutes for softly set eggs.
6. Divide between plates and serve hot.

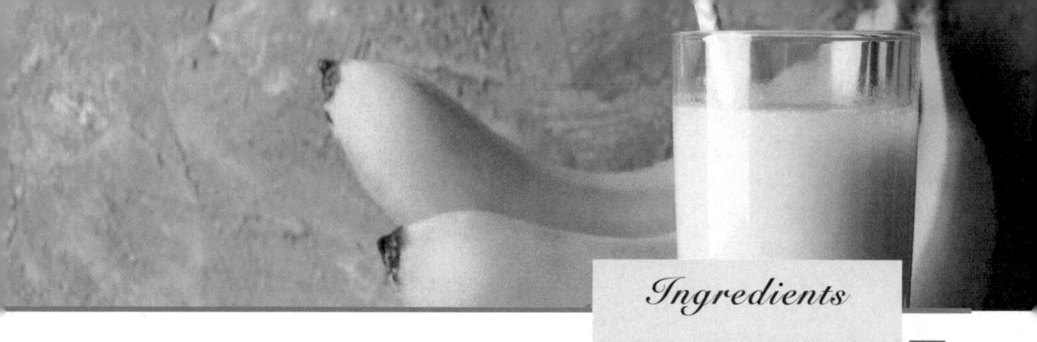

BANANA SMOOTHIE

Servings:	**Prep Time:**	**Cook Time:**
1	5 mins	5 mins

Description:
A smoothie packed with protein and potassium to fuel your morning without weighing you down.weighing you down.

Ingredients

- 1 large banana
- 2 tbsp. natural peanut butter
- 1 cup unsweetened almond milk
- 1/2 tsp. vanilla extract
- Ice cubes (optional)

Breakfast

Preparation steps:

1. Place the banana, peanut butter, almond milk, vanilla extract, and ice cubes if using, in a blender.
2. Blend on high until smooth and creamy.
3. Pour into a glass and serve immediately for a refreshing and energizing breakfast smoothie.

Breakfast

Ingredients

- 1 cup low-fat cottage cheese
- 1/2 cup chopped pineapple
- 1 tbsp. chopped almonds
- 1 tsp. honey (optional)

COTTAGE & PINEAPPLE BOWL

Servings: 1

Prep Time: 5 Mins

Cook Time: 5 mins

Description:

A protein-rich bowl featuring creamy cottage paired with tangy pineapple chunks, ideal for a quick and nutritious breakfast.

Preparation steps:

1. In a bowl, combine the cottage cheese and pineapple.
2. Sprinkle with chopped almonds for crunch.
3. Drizzle with honey if desired for a touch of sweetness.
4. Mix gently and serve immediately for a refreshing, protein-packed start to your day.

Breakfast

SPINACH AND QUINOA BOWLS

Servings: 2	**Prep Time:** 10 mins	**Cook Time:** 20 mins

Description:
A healthful bowl filled with cooked quinoa, sautéed spinach, and a hint of garlic, topped with a poached egg for added protein.

Ingredients

- 1 cup cooked quinoa
- 2 cups fresh spinach
- 2 large eggs
- 2 cloves garlic, minced
- 2 tbsp. olive oil
- Salt and pepper to taste

Preparation steps:

1. Heat olive oil in a skillet over medium heat. Add the minced garlic and sauté until fragrant, about 1 minute.
2. Add the spinach and cook until wilted, about 3-4 minutes. Season with salt and pepper.
3. Divide the cooked quinoa between two bowls. Top each with the sautéed spinach.
4. Poach the eggs by gently dropping them into simmering water for about 4 minutes, or until the whites are set but the yolks remain runny.
5. Place a poached egg on top of each quinoa and spinach bowl.
6. Serve immediately ok go on with the starter recipes. do not repete recipes that you already wrote

Starters

Ingredients

- 4 cups broccoli florets
- 1 medium onion, diced
- 2 cloves garlic, minced
- 2 cups low-sodium vegetable broth
- 1 cup low-fat milk
- 1/2 cup shredded low-fat cheddar cheese
- Salt and pepper to taste
- 1 tbsp. olive oil

BROCCOLI AND CHEDDAR SOUP

Servings: 4

Prep Time: 10 Mins

Cook Time: 20 mins

Description:
A creamy, low-fat version of a classic soup using pureed broccoli and low-fat cheddar for a comforting starter.

Preparation steps:

1. Heat olive oil in a large pot over medium heat. Add onion and garlic, sautéing until soft, about 5 minutes.
2. Add broccoli and vegetable broth, bring to a boil, then reduce heat and simmer until broccoli is tender, about 10 minutes.
3. Puree the mixture using an immersion blender until smooth.
4. Stir in milk and cheddar cheese until the cheese is melted and the soup is heated through. Season with salt and pepper.
5. Serve warm as a light but satisfying starter.

CUCUMBER AND HUMMUS BITES

Servings:
6

Prep Time:
10 mins

Cook Time:
5 mins

Description:
Crisp cucumber slices topped with savory hummus and a sprinkle of paprika, perfect for a refreshing and healthy appetizer.

Ingredients

- 2 large cucumbers, sliced thickly
- 1 cup hummus
- Paprika for garnish
- Fresh parsley, chopped (optional)

Starters

Preparation steps:

1. Arrange cucumber slices on a serving platter.
2. Top each slice with a spoonful of hummus.
3. Sprinkle with paprika and optional chopped parsley for color and flavor.
4. Serve immediately or chill until serving for a crisp, cool appetizer.

Starters

Ingredients

- 2 cups canned chickpeas, drained and rinsed
- 1 tbsp. olive oil
- 1 tsp. chili powder
- 1/2 tsp. cumin
- Salt to taste

SPICY ROASTED CHICKPEAS

Servings: 4

Prep Time: 5 Mins

Cook Time: 30 mins

Description:

Oven-roasted chickpeas tossed in a spic seasoning mix, making them a crunchy an protein-packed snack or starter.

Preparation steps:

1. Preheat oven to 400°F (200°C).
2. Dry the chickpeas with paper towels, removing as much moisture as possible.
3. Toss chickpeas in olive oil, chili powder, cumin, and salt until evenly coated.
4. Spread chickpeas on a baking sheet in a single layer.
5. Roast in the preheated oven for 30 minutes, shaking the pan occasionally to ensure even cooking.
6. Remove from oven once crispy and golden. Let cool slightly before serving.

KALE AND APPLE SALAD

Servings: 4

Prep Time: 15 mins

Cook Time: 5 mins

Description:
A fresh salad, dressed with a homemade mustard vinaigrette, ideal for a light and nutritious start to any meal.

Ingredients

- 4 cups chopped kale
- 2 apples, cored and thinly sliced
- 1/4 cup dried cranberries
- 1/4 cup sliced almonds
- 3 tbsp. olive oil
- 1 tbsp. apple cider vinegar
- 1 tbsp. Dijon mustard
- 1 tsp. honey
- Salt and pepper to taste

Preparation steps:

1. In a large bowl, combine the chopped kale, sliced apples, dried cranberries, and sliced almonds.
2. In a small bowl, whisk together olive oil, apple cider vinegar, Dijon mustard, honey, salt, and pepper to create the vinaigrette.
3. Drizzle the vinaigrette over the salad and toss to coat evenly.
4. Let the salad sit for about 10 minutes before serving to allow the kale to soften slightly.

Starters

Ingredients

- 2 large zucchinis, thinly sliced
- 1 tbsp. olive oil
- Salt to taste

ZUCCHINI CHIPS

Servings:
4

Prep Time:
10 Mins

Cook Time:
20 mins

Description:

Zucchini chips baked until crispy, a low-calorie and nutritious alternative to tradition chips, perfect for snacking or as a starter.

Preparation steps:

1. Preheat oven to 425°F (220°C).
2. In a bowl, toss the zucchini slices with olive oi and salt.
3. Arrange slices in a single layer on a baking shee lined with parchment paper.
4. Bake in the preheated oven for 20-25 minutes flipping the slices halfway through until they are golden and crispy.
5. Remove from oven and let cool on a wire rack to maintain crispness. Serve immediately.

STUFFED CHERRY TOMATOES

Servings:
6

Prep Time:
20 mins

Cook Time:
mins

Description:
Cherry tomatoes stuffed with a mix of feta cheese, herbs, and olives, for a burst of Mediterranean flavors in a bite-sized appetizer.

Ingredients

- 24 cherry tomatoes
- 1/2 cup crumbled feta cheese
- 1/4 cup chopped black olives
- 2 tbsp. chopped fresh basil
- 1 tbsp. olive oil
- Salt and pepper to taste

Preparation steps:

1. Slice the tops off the cherry tomatoes and scoop out the insides to create a hollow space.
2. In a small bowl, mix together feta cheese, black olives, basil, olive oil, salt, and pepper.
3. Carefully stuff the mixture into the hollowed-out tomatoes.
4. Chill in the refrigerator until ready to serve, allowing the flavors to meld together.

Starters

Ingredients

- 1 pound cooked shrimp, peeled and deveined
- 1 ripe avocado, diced
- 1/2 red onion, finely chopped
- 1/4 cup chopped cilantro
- Juice of 2 limes
- Juice of 1 orange
- 1 jalapeño, seeded and finely chopped (optional)
- Salt and pepper

AVOCADO SHRIMP CEVICHE

Servings: 4

Prep Time: 15 Mins

Cook Time: 5 mins

Description:
A refreshing and light ceviche with shrimp and avocado, marinated in citrus juices, perfect for a nutritious and flavorful starter.

Preparation steps:

1. In a large bowl, combine the shrimp, avocado, red onion, cilantro, and jalapeño if using.
2. Pour over the lime and orange juice, ensuring the ingredients are well coated.
3. Season with salt and pepper to taste.
4. Cover and let marinate in the refrigerator for about 30 minutes to allow the flavors to blend.
5. Serve chilled, garnished with additional cilantro if desired.

BEETROOT & GOAT CHEESE SALAD

Servings:	Prep Time:	Cook Time:
4	10 mins	5 mins

Description:

Earthy beetroots paired with tangy goat cheese and a balsamic glaze, offering a delicious and visually stunning salad option.

Ingredients

- 4 medium beetroots, cooked and sliced
- 1/4 cup crumbled goat cheese
- 2 tbsp. chopped walnuts
- 2 cups mixed salad greens
- 2 tbsp. balsamic glaze

Preparation steps:

1. Arrange the salad greens on a serving plate.
2. Top with sliced beetroots and crumbled goat cheese.
3. Sprinkle chopped walnuts over the top for added texture.
4. Drizzle with balsamic glaze just before serving.
5. Serve as a colorful and nutritious starter or side dish.

Starters

Ingredients

- 1 tbsp. olive oil
- 1 onion, chopped
- 4 cups chopped carrots
- 2 tbsp. grated fresh ginger
- 4 cups vegetable broth
- Salt and pepper to taste

CARROT AND GINGER SOUP

Servings:
4

Prep Time:
10 Mins

Cook Time:
20 mins

Description:

A smooth and warming soup made fro carrots and ginger, providing an immu ne-boosting dish ideal for any starter.

Preparation steps:

1. Heat the olive oil in a large pot over medium heat.
2. Add the chopped onion and sauté until translucent, about 5 minutes.
3. Add the carrots and grated ginger, cooking for another 5 minutes.
4. Pour in the vegetable broth and bring to a boil. Reduce heat and simmer until carrots are tender, about 15 minutes.
5. Blend the soup using an immersion blender until smooth.
6. Season with salt and pepper to taste.
7. Serve hot, garnished with a swirl of cream or a sprinkle of chopped herbs if desired.

CAPRESE SKEWERS

Servings: 6

Prep Time: 10 mins

Cook Time: 5 mins

Ingredients

- 12 cherry tomatoes
- 12 small mozzarella balls
- 12 fresh basil leaves
- Balsamic glaze
- Salt and pepper to taste

Starters

Description:

A simple yet elegant starter featuring fresh cherry tomatoes, mozzarella, and basil, for a classic Italian flavor.

Preparation steps:

1. Thread a cherry tomato, a basil leaf, and a mozzarella ball onto each skewer.
2. Arrange the skewers on a platter.
3. Drizzle with balsamic glaze and season with salt and pepper.
4. Serve chilled or at room temperature as a delightful and refreshing appetizer.

Starters

Ingredients

- 2 large cucumbers
- 4 ounces smoked salmon, chopped
- 2 ounces cream cheese, softened
- Fresh dill for garnish
- 1 tbsp. lemon juice
- Salt and pepper to taste

SMOKED SALMON & CREAM CUPS

Servings: 4

Prep Time: 15 Mins

Cook Time: 5 mins

Description:

Elegant cucumber cups filled with smoke salmon and a touch of cream, garnished wit dill for a light appetizer.

Preparation steps:

1. Peel the cucumbers and cut into 1-inch thick slices. Hollow out the centers of each slice using a melon baller or small spoon, leaving the bottom intact to create a cup.
2. In a small bowl, mix the smoked salmon with cream cheese and lemon juice until well combined. Season with salt and pepper.
3. Spoon the salmon mixture into the cucumber cups.
4. Garnish with small sprigs of fresh dill.
5. Chill in the refrigerator for about 30 minutes before serving to let the flavors meld.

GRILLED VEGETABLE PLATTER

Servings: 4

Prep Time: 15 mins

Cook Time: 15 mins

Description:

A vibrant assortment of grilled vegetables served with a refreshing herbed yogurt dip, perfect for a light and healthy starter.

Ingredients

- 1 zucchini, sliced
- 1 bell pepper, cut into pieces
- 1 eggplant, sliced
- 1 red onion, cut into wedges
- Olive oil for brushing
- 1 cup Greek yogurt
- 2 tbsp. chopped fresh herbs (parsley, dill, or mint)
- 1 clove garlic

Preparation steps:

1. Preheat the grill to medium-high heat.
2. Brush the vegetables with olive oil and season with salt and pepper.
3. Grill the vegetables until tender and charred, about 3-5 minutes per side.
4. While the vegetables are grilling, prepare the dip by combining Greek yogurt, chopped herbs, minced garlic, and a pinch of salt in a bowl. Mix well.
5. Arrange the grilled vegetables on a platter and serve with the herbed yogurt dip.

EDAMAME WITH SEA SALT

Starters

Ingredients

- 2 cups frozen edamame in pods
- Sea salt to taste

Servings:
4

Prep Time:
5 Mins

Cook Time:
5 mins

Description:

Steamed edamame sprinkled with sea salt, simple and protein-rich snack that's both satisfying and heart-healthy.

Preparation steps:

1. Bring a pot of water to a boil.
2. Add the frozen edamame and cook for abou 5 minutes, or until fully heated through and tender.
3. Drain the edamame and sprinkle with sea salt.
4. Serve warm or at room temperature as a snack or a light appetizer.

ROASTED RED PEPPER HUMMUS

Servings: 6

Prep Time: 10 mins

Cook Time: 5 mins

Description:

Homemade hummus enhanced with the smoky flavor of roasted red peppers, perfect for dipping vegetables or whole-wheat pita.

Ingredients

- 1 can (15 oz) chickpeas, drained and rinsed
- 1 large roasted red pepper (jarred or homemade)
- 2 tbsp. tahini
- 2 cloves garlic, minced
- Juice of 1 lemon
- 2 tbsp. olive oil
- Salt and paprika to taste

Preparation steps:

1. In a food processor, combine chickpeas, roasted red pepper, tahini, garlic, lemon juice, and olive oil.
2. Process until smooth, adding a little water if needed to achieve the desired consistency.
3. Season with salt and paprika.
4. Transfer to a serving bowl and serve with a drizzle of olive oil and a sprinkle of paprika on top, accompanied by your choice of crudites or pita bread.

Starters

Ingredients

- 4 cups mixed greens (such as arugula and spinach)
- 2 ripe pears, thinly sliced
- 1/2 cup walnuts, toasted
- 1/4 cup crumbled Gorgonzola cheese
- 3 tbsp. balsamic vinegar
- 1 tbsp. honey
- 1 tbsp. olive oil
- Salt and pepper

PEAR AND WALNUT SALAD

Servings: 4

Prep Time: 15 Mins

Cook Time: 5 mins

Description:

A crisp and refreshing salad combinin sweet pears, walnuts, and creamy Gorgonzc la, dressed in a light balsamic vinaigrette.

Preparation steps:

1. In a large bowl, toss the mixed greens with the sliced pears, toasted walnuts, and Gorgonzola cheese.
2. In a small bowl, whisk together the balsamic vinegar, honey, olive oil, salt, and pepper to create the dressing.
3. Drizzle the dressing over the salad and toss gently to coat all the ingredients evenly.
4. Serve immediately, offering a delightful blend of textures and flavors that make for a perfect starter or light meal.

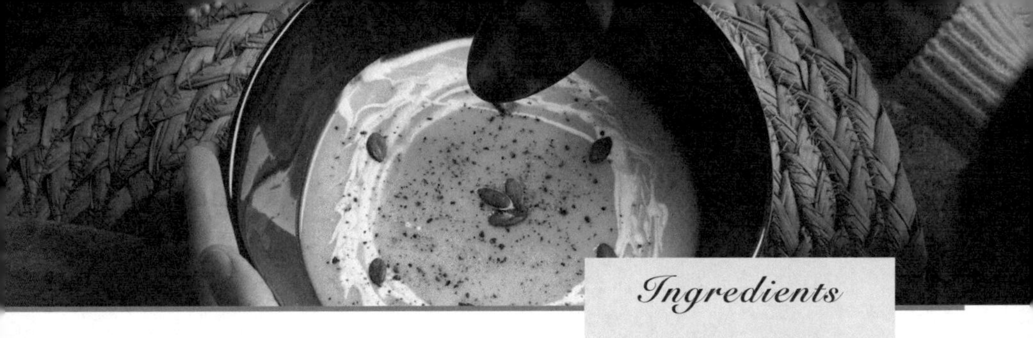

SPICED PUMPKIN SOUP

Servings: 4

Prep Time: 10 mins

Cook Time: 25 mins

Description:

A creamy and comforting soup made with pumpkin and aromatic spices, perfect for a warm, inviting start to any meal.

Ingredients

- 2 tbsp. olive oil
- 1 onion, chopped
- 2 cloves garlic
- 1 tsp. ground cumin
- 1/2 tsp. coriander
- 4 cups pumpkin puree (fresh or canned)
- 4 cups vegetable broth
- Salt and pepper to taste
- 1/2 cup light cream (optional)

Preparation steps:

1. Heat olive oil in a large pot over medium heat.
2. Add the chopped onion and garlic, cooking until the onion is translucent, about 5 minutes.
3. Stir in the cumin and coriander, cooking for an additional minute until fragrant.
4. Add the pumpkin pure and vegetable broth, bringing the mixture to a boil.
5. Reduce heat and simmer for 20 minutes, allowing the flavors to meld together.
6. Blend the soup using an immersion blender until smooth.
7. Stir in the light cream if using, and heat through. Season with salt and pepper to taste.
8. Serve hot, garnished with a swirl of cream sprinkle of roasted pumpkin seeds for added texture.

Ingredients

- 4 boneless, skinless chicken breasts
- 1 cup quinoa
- 2 cups chicken broth
- 1/4 cup chopped fresh herbs (parsley, basil, thyme)
- 2 tbsp. olive oil
- Salt and pepper to taste
- Lemon wedges for serving

GRILLED CHICKEN & QUINOA

Servings: 4

Prep Time: 15 Mins

Cook Time: 20 mins

Description:

Juicy grilled chicken served over a bed of flu ffy quinoa seasoned with fresh herbs, a ba lanced dish high in protein and fiber.

Preparation steps:

1. Rinse quinoa under cold water and drain.
2. In a saucepan, bring chicken broth to a boil. Add quinoa, reduce heat to low, cover, and simmer for 15 minutes or until all liquid is absorbed.
3. Remove from heat, fluff with a fork, and stir in the chopped herbs.
4. While the quinoa cooks, heat a grill or grill pan over medium-high heat. Rub chicken breast with olive oil, salt, and pepper.
5. Grill the chicken for about 6-7 minutes per side or until fully cooked and internal temperature reaches 165°F (74°C).
6. Serve the grilled chicken over the herbed quinoa with lemon wedges on the side.

SALMON WITH ASPARAGUS

Servings: 4

Prep Time: 10 mins

Cook Time: 20 mins

Description:

Oven-baked salmon fillets with a touch of lemon, served alongside steamed asparagus, a meal rich in omega-3 fatty acids and vitamins.

Ingredients

- 4 salmon fillets (6 oz each)
- 1 lb asparagus, ends trimmed
- 2 tbsp. olive oil
- Salt and pepper to taste
- Lemon slices for garnish

Main Dishes

Preparation steps:

1. Preheat oven to 400°F (200°C).
2. Place salmon fillets on a baking sheet lined with parchment paper. Drizzle with 1 tbsp. olive oil, season with salt and pepper, and top each with a lemon slice.
3. Bake for 15-20 minutes or until salmon is cooked through and flakes easily with a fork.
4. Meanwhile, steam asparagus in a steamer basket over boiling water for about 5-7 minutes or until tender yet crisp.
5. Drizzle the remaining olive oil over the asparagus, season with salt and pepper.
6. Serve the salmon and asparagus together, garnished with additional lemon slices if desired.

Ingredients

- 1 pound ground turkey
- 1/4 cup breadcrumbs
- 1/4 cup grated Parmesan cheese
- 1 egg
- 2 cloves garlic, minced
- 1 tsp. dried Italian herbs
- Salt and pepper to taste
- 2 cups tomato sauce
- 1 tbsp. olive oil

TURKEY MEATBALLS IN SAUCE

Servings: 4

Prep Time: 20 Mins

Cook Time: 30 mins

Description:

Lean turkey meatballs simmered in a homemade tomato sauce, a comforting dish that's both low in fat and high in flavor.

Preparation steps:

1. In a bowl, combine ground turkey, breadcrumbs, Parmesan, egg, garlic, Italian herbs, salt, and pepper. Mix well.
2. Form the mixture into 1-inch meatballs.
3. Heat olive oil in a large skillet over medium heat. Add meatballs and brown on all sides, about 5-7 minutes.
4. Pour tomato sauce over the meatballs. Reduce heat to low and simmer for 20 minutes, or until meatballs are cooked through.
5. Serve hot, garnished with extra grated Parmesan and fresh basil if desired.

VEGETARIAN STUFFED PEPPERS

Servings: 4

Prep Time: 20 mins

Cook Time: 30 mins

Description:

Bell peppers stuffed with a savory mix of quinoa, black beans, corn, and spices, topped with melted cheese, a filling vegetarian meal.

Ingredients

- 4 bell peppers
- 1 cup cooked quinoa
- 1 can (15 oz) black beans, rinsed and drained
- 1 cup corn kernels
- 1/2 cup onion
- 2 cloves garlic
- 1 tsp. cumin
- 1/2 tsp. chili
- 1 cup shredded low-fat cheese
- 2 tbsp. olive oil

Preparation steps:

1. Preheat oven to 375°F (190°C).
2. In a skillet, heat the olive oil. Sauté the onion and garlic until soft, about 5 minutes.
3. Add the cumin and chili powder, stirring for another minute to release the flavors.
4. Stir in the cooked quinoa, black beans, and corn. Season with salt and pepper. Cook for another 5 minutes, stirring occasionally.
5. Fill each bell pepper with the quinoa mixture and place them in a baking dish.
6. Top each stuffed pepper with shredded cheese.
7. Cover the dish with aluminum foil and bake in the preheated oven for 25 minutes.
8. Remove the foil and bake for an additional 5 minutes or until the cheese is melted and bubbly.
9. Serve the stuffed peppers hot and guarnish.

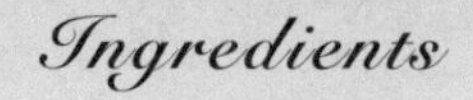

- 1 pound chicken breast
- 1 can (14 oz) coconut milk
- 2 tbsp. green curry
- chicken broth
- 1 bell pepper
- 1 cup snap peas
- 1 small eggplant
- 1 tbsp. fish sauce
- 1 tsp. sugar
- 2 tbsp. vegetable oil
- Fresh basil leaves for garnish

GREEN CURRY WITH CHICKEN

Servings: 4

Prep Time: 15 Mins

Cook Time: 20 mins

Description:

Aromatic and spicy Thai green curry mac with coconut milk, and a variety of veget bles, offering a flavorful and satisfying mea

Preparation steps:

1. Heat the vegetable oil in a large skillet or wok over medium-high heat.
2. Add the green curry paste and stir for about 1 minute until aromatic.
3. Add the chicken pieces and brown them, ensurin they are coated with the curry paste.
4. Pour in the coconut milk and chicken broth bringing the mixture to a simmer.
5. Add the bell pepper, snap peas, and eggplant Cook for about 10 minutes, or until th vegetables are tender and the chicken is cooke through.
6. Stir in the fish sauce and sugar. Adjust seasonin to taste.

HERB-CRUSTED RACK OF LAMB

Servings:	**Prep Time:**	**Cook Time:**
4	20 mins	25 mins

Ingredients

- 1 rack of lamb (about 8 ribs)
- 1/4 cup fresh breadcrumbs
- 2 tbsp. chopped fresh rosemary
- 2 tbsp. chopped fresh thyme
- 2 cloves garlic, minced
- 2 tbsp. olive oil
- Salt and pepper to taste

Description:

A succulent lamb encrusted with a blend of fresh herbs and garlic, roasted to perfection, ideal for a special occasion or gourmet meal.

Preparation steps:

1. Preheat the oven to 400°F (200°C).
2. Season the rack of lamb with salt and pepper.
3. In a small bowl, mix together breadcrumbs, rosemary, thyme, garlic, and olive oil to create a paste.
4. Coat the lamb evenly with the herb mixture.
5. Place the lamb in a roasting pan, bone side down, and roast in the preheated oven for 25 minutes or until the meat reaches your desired level of doneness.
6. Let the lamb rest for 10 minutes before carving between the ribs.
7. Serve the lamb chops with a side of roasted vegetables or a fresh salad.

LEMON BUTTER SCALLOPS

Ingredients

- 16 large sea scallops, patted dry
- 2 tbsp. unsalted butter
- Juice of 1 lemon
- 1 tsp. minced garlic
- 2 tbsp. chopped fresh parsley
- Salt and black pepper to taste
- 2 tbsp. olive oil

Servings: 4

Prep Time: 10 Mins

Cook Time: 10 mins

Description:

Tender scallops seared with a zesty lemon butter sauce, a luxurious yet simple dish low in carbs and high in protein.

Preparation steps:

1. Heat olive oil in a large skillet over high heat until very hot.
2. Season scallops with salt and pepper. Place scallops in the skillet in a single layer, and sear for about 2 minutes on each side or until a golden crust forms.
3. Remove scallops from skillet and set aside.
4. Reduce heat to medium, add butter and garlic to the skillet, and sauté for about 1 minute until garlic is fragrant.
5. Add lemon juice and half of the parsley, stir to combine, and cook for another minute.
6. Return scallops to the skillet, spooning the sauce over them to warm through.

VEGAN MUSHROOM RISOTTO

Servings: 4

Prep Time: 10 mins

Cook Time: 25 mins

Description:

A creamy and satisfying risotto made with arborio rice, assorted mushrooms, and vegetable
broth, perfect for a hearty vegan meal.

Ingredients

- 1 cup arborio rice
- egetable broth
- 1 onion
- 2 cups mixed mushrooms, sliced (shiitake, portobello, or button)
- 2 cloves garlic, minced
- 2 tbsp. olive oil
- 1/4 cup nutritional yeast
- Fresh thyme for garnish
- Fresh thyme

Main Dishes

Preparation steps:

1. Heat olive oil in a large pan over medium heat. Add onion and garlic, sauté until translucent.
2. Add mushrooms and cook until they begin to soften and brown.
3. Stir in arborio rice, toasting it lightly for about 2 minutes.
4. If using, deglaze the pan with white wine and allow it to absorb fully.
5. Gradually add heated vegetable broth, one cup at a time, stirring constantly until each cup is absorbed before adding the next.
6. Once all the broth is absorbed and the rice is al dente, stir in nutritional yeast, and season with salt and pepper.

Ingredients

- 1 pound beef sirloin
- 2 cups broccoli florets
- 1 red bell pepper
- 1 green bell pepper, sliced
- 2 tbsp. soy sauce
- 1 tbsp. sesame oil
- 2 cloves garlic
- 1 tbsp. fresh ginger
- vegetable oil
- Sesame seeds garnish

BEEF STIR-FRY & VEGETABLES

Servings:	Prep Time:	Cook Time:
4	15 Mins	10 mins

Description:

Stir-fry tender beef strips with broccoli and bell peppers, seasoned with soy sauce and sesame oil for an Asian-inspired meal.

Preparation steps:

1. Heat vegetable oil in a large skillet or wok over high heat.
2. Add garlic and ginger, sauté for about 30 seconds until fragrant.
3. Add beef strips and stir-fry for about 3-4 minutes until they start to brown.
4. Add broccoli and bell peppers, continuing to stir-fry for another 5 minutes until vegetables are tender-crisp and beef is cooked through.
5. Drizzle with soy sauce and sesame oil, toss to coat evenly.
6. Serve immediately, sprinkled with sesame seeds.

GLAZED PORK TENDERLOIN

Servings: 4

Prep Time: 15 mins

Cook Time: 25 mins

Description:

Pork tenderloin roasted to perfection with a sweet and tangy apple cider glaze, it marries the flavors of autumn with healthy eating.

Ingredients

- 1 pork tenderloin (about 1 pound)
- 1 cup apple cider
- 2 tbsp. apple cider vinegar
- 2 tbsp. honey
- 1 tsp. mustard
- 1/2 tsp. salt
- 1/4 tsp. black pepper
- 2 tbsp. olive oil
- Fresh herbs (such as rosemary or thyme) for garnish

Main Dishes

Preparation steps:

1. Preheat oven to 375°F (190°C).
2. In a small saucepan, combine apple cider, apple cider vinegar, honey, and mustard. Reduce by half until thickened into a glaze (10-15 min).
3. While the glaze is reducing, season the pork tenderloin with salt and pepper.
4. Heat olive oil in a large oven-proof skillet over medium-high heat. Sear the tenderloin on all sides until golden brown, about 5-7 minutes.
5. Brush the tenderloin with half of the cider glaze and place in the oven.
6. Roast for about 15-20 min, or reaches an internal temperature of 145°F (63°C). Halfway through, brush with the remaining glaze.
7. Let the pork rest for 5 minutes before slicing. Serve garnished with fresh herbs.

Ingredients

- 2 large heads of cauliflower
- 1/2 cup walnuts
- 1/2 cup fresh basil leaves
- 1/4 cup grated Parmesan cheese
- 2 cloves garlic
- 1/2 cup olive oil
- Salt and pepper to taste

CAULIFLOWER STEAK & PESTO

Servings: 4

Prep Time: 10 Mins

Cook Time: 20 mins

Description:
Thick slices of cauliflower roasted and to pped with a homemade walnut pesto, a vege tarian dish that's hearty and flavorful.

Preparation steps:

1. Preheat oven to 400°F (200°C).
2. Slice cauliflower heads vertically into 1-inch thick steaks.
3. Place cauliflower steaks on a baking sheet, drizzle with 2 tbsp. olive oil, and season with salt and pepper.
4. Roast in the preheated oven for about 20 minutes, flipping halfway, until tender and golden.
5. Meanwhile, in a food processor, combine walnuts, basil, Parmesan, garlic, and remaining olive oil. Blend until smooth to make the pesto.
6. Serve cauliflower steaks with a generous dollop of walnut pesto on top.

SHRIMP & ASPARAGUS STIR-FRY

Servings: 4

Prep Time: 10 mins

Cook Time: 10 mins

Description:

A light stir-fry featuring shrimp and asparagus, flavored with garlic and lemon, perfect for a quick and healthy dinner.

Ingredients

- 1 pound large shrimp, peeled and deveined
- 1 pound asparagus, trimmed and cut into 2-inch pieces
- 3 cloves garlic, minced
- Juice of 1 lemon
- 2 tbsp. olive oil
- Salt and pepper to taste
- Lemon wedges for serving

Preparation steps:

1. Heat olive oil in a large skillet over medium-high heat.
2. Add garlic and sauté for about 30 seconds until fragrant.
3. Add asparagus and cook for about 4 minutes until just tender.
4. Add shrimp and cook for about 3-4 minutes, or until shrimp are pink and cooked through.
5. Squeeze lemon juice over the top, season with salt and pepper, and stir to combine.
6. Serve immediately with additional lemon wedges on the side.

Main Dishes

Ingredients

- 4 chicken breasts
- 2 tsp.s paprika
- 1 tsp. cumin
- 1/2 tsp. cinnamon
- 1/2 tsp. ginger
- 1/4 tsp. pepper
- 2 tbsp. olive oil
- 1 cup couscous
- 1-1/2 cups chicken broth
- 1 cup chopped carrots
- 1 cup zucchin
- 1/2 cup raisins
- Fresh cilantro chopped, for

MOROCCAN CHICKEN COUSCOUS

Servings: 4

Prep Time: 20 Mins

Cook Time: 30 mins

Description:

Moroccan-inspired chicken dish, served wit fluffy couscous and a medley of vegetable offering a taste of North Africa.

Preparation steps:

1. In a small bowl, mix together paprika, cumin, cinnamon, ginger, cayenne, salt, and pepper. Rub this spice mix all over the chicken breasts.
2. Heat olive oil in a large skillet over medium heat. Add the chicken and cook until golden and cooked through, about 6-7 minutes per side Remove from skillet and keep warm.
3. In the same skillet, add carrots and zucchini, and sauté until they start to soften, about 5 minutes
4. Add chicken broth to the skillet and bring to a boil. Stir in couscous and raisins, remove from heat, cover, and let sit for 5 minutes, or until al liquid is absorbed.
5. Fluff the couscous with a fork, mixing in the

LEMON HERB TILAPIA

Servings:	**Prep Time:**	**Cook Time:**
4	10 mins	15 mins

Description:
Flaky tilapia fillets, seasoned with lemon and herbs, served alongside crisp green beans, a perfect meal for maintaining a healthy diet.

Ingredients

- 4 tilapia fillets
- Juice of 2 lemons
- 2 tbsp. chopped fresh herbs (parsley, dill, or basil)
- 4 tbsp. olive oil
- 1 pound green beans, trimmed
- Salt and pepper to taste
- Lemon slices for garnish

Main Dishes

Preparation steps:

1. Preheat oven to 400°F (200°C).
2. In a small bowl, mix together lemon juice, herbs, and 2 tbsp. olive oil.
3. Place tilapia fillets on a baking sheet lined with parchment paper. Season with salt and pepper, then drizzle with half of the lemon herb mixture.
4. In another bowl, toss green beans with the remaining olive oil, salt, and pepper. Spread around the tilapia on the baking sheet.
5. Bake for 12-15 minutes, until the tilapia is cooked through and the green beans are tender.
6. Serve the tilapia and green beans with the remaining lemon herb mixture drizzled over and garnish with lemon slices.

Ingredients

- 1 pound flank steak
- 4 cups broccoli
- 2 cloves garlic
- 1 tbsp. ginger
- 1/4 cup soy sauce
- 1 tbsp. oyster sauce
- 1 tbsp. sesame oil
- 1 tbsp. cornstarch
- 1/2 cup beef broth
- 2 tbsp. vegetable oil

BEEF AND BROCCOLI STIR-FRY

Servings:
4

Prep Time:
15 Mins

Cook Time:
10 mins

Description:

Chinese dish, this stir-fry combines bee strips with broccoli in a savory sauce, quic and easy for a nutritious weeknight dinner.

Preparation steps:

1. In a small bowl, mix cornstarch, beef broth, soy sauce, oyster sauce, and sesame oil to make the sauce.
2. Heat vegetable oil in a large skillet or wok over high heat. Add garlic and ginger, sauté for about 30 seconds.
3. Add the beef and stir-fry until it starts to brown, about 3-4 minutes.
4. Add broccoli and stir-fry for another 3-4 minutes until the vegetables are tender and the beef is cooked through.
5. Pour the sauce over the beef and broccoli, stirring continuously until the sauce thickens and coats the ingredients evenly.
6. Serve immediately, offering a tasty and wholesome meal.

RATATOUILLE WITH POLENTA

Servings: 4

Prep Time: 20 mins

Cook Time: 40 mins

Description:

Classic French vegetable stew paired with creamy baked polenta, both comforting and heart-healthy, packed with fresh produce.

Ingredients

- 1 zucchini
- 1 eggplant
- 2 red bell pepper
- 2 tomatoes
- 1 onion
- 3 cloves garlic
- 1/4 cup olive oil
- 1 tsp. dried thyme
- 1 tsp. dried basil
- 1 cup polenta
- 4 cups water
- 1 tbsp. butter
- 1/4 cup grated Parmesan cheese

Preparation steps:

1. Preheat oven to 375°F (190°C).
2. In a large baking dish, combine zucchini, eggplant, bell peppers, tomatoes, onion, and garlic. Drizzle with olive oil and sprinkle with thyme, basil, salt, and pepper.
3. Bake in the preheated oven for about 35 minutes, stirring occasionally, until vegetables are tender.
4. Meanwhile, bring water to a boil in a saucepan. Gradually whisk in polenta, reduce heat to low, and cook, stirring frequently, until polenta is thick and creamy, about 15-20 minutes.
5. Stir in butter and Parmesan cheese.
6. Pour polenta into a greased baking dish and bake for about 20 minutes, or until set
7. Serve the ratatouille over slices of baked polenta, offering a hearty and nutritious meal.

Main Dishes

Ingredients

- 4 duck breasts, skin scored
- Salt and pepper to taste
- 1/2 cup fresh orange juice
- 2 tbsp. honey
- 1 tbsp. soy sauce
- 1 clove garlic, minced
- 1 tsp. grated ginger
- 2 tbsp. olive oil

GLAZED PAN-SEARED DUCK

Servings:	**Prep Time:**	**Cook Time:**
4	15 Mins	20 mins

Description:

Duck breast topped with a orange glaze, a elegant option for a special dinner, rich flavors and a touch of sophistication.

Preparation steps:

1. Season duck breasts with salt and pepper.
2. Heat olive oil in a skillet over medium-high heat. Place duck breasts skin-side down and cook until the skin is crisp and golden, about 6-7 minutes. Turn and cook the other side for about 5 minutes, or until desired doneness.
3. Remove duck from skillet and let rest.
4. In the same skillet, reduce heat to medium. Add orange juice, honey, soy sauce, garlic, and ginger. Simmer until the sauce thickens into a glaze, about 5-7 minutes
5. Pour the orange glaze over the rested duck breasts, ensuring each piece is evenly coated.
6. Serve the duck breasts sliced, with extra glaze drizzled over the top for added flavor.

GRILLED TOFU STEAKS & AVOCADO

Servings: 4

Prep Time: 10 mins

Cook Time: 10 mins

Description:
Marinated tofu grilled tand topped with a fresh avocado salsa, a delicious vegan-friendly dish that's rich in protein and healthy fats.

Ingredients

- 4 thick slices tofu, pressed and drained
- 2 tbsp. soy sauce
- 1 tbsp. lime juice
- 1 tbsp. olive oil
- 1 tsp. chili powder
- 1 ripe avocado
- 1 small tomato
- 1/4 cup red onion
- 1/4 cup fresh cilantro

Preparation steps:

1. In a small bowl, mix soy sauce, lime juice, olive oil, and chili powder to create the marinade.
2. Place tofu slices in a shallow dish and pour the marinade over them. Let marinate for at least 30 minutes in the refrigerator.
3. Preheat a grill or grill pan over medium heat. Remove tofu from marinade and grill for about 5 minutes on each side, or until grill marks appear and tofu is heated through.
4. In another bowl, combine diced avocado, tomato, red onion, and cilantro. Season with salt and pepper to taste.
5. Serve grilled tofu steaks topped with the fresh avocado salsa.

COD EN PAPILLOTE

Ingredients

- 4 cod fillets
- 1 zucchini, thinly sliced
- 1 carrot, thinly sliced
- 1 leek, thinly sliced
- 1/2 cup white wine
- 4 tbsp. olive oil
- Salt and pepper to taste
- Fresh dill or parsley, for garnish

Servings: 4

Prep Time: 20 Mins

Cook Time: 15 mins

Description:
Cod fillets and vegetables cooked in parchment paper with white wine, a flavorful and moist dish that's light and healthy.

Preparation steps:

1. Preheat oven to 400°F (200°C).
2. Cut four large pieces of parchment paper. Place a cod fillet in the center of each piece.
3. Top each fillet with equal portions of zucchini, carrot, and leek. Drizzle with olive oil and white wine. Season with salt and pepper.
4. Fold the parchment paper over the ingredients, sealing the edges tightly to form a packet.
5. Place the packets on a baking sheet and bake for about 15 minutes, or until the fish is cooked through and vegetables are tender.
6. Serve immediately, opening the packets at the table to release the steam and aromas, garnished with fresh herbs.

LAMB KOFTAS WITH TZATZIKI

Servings: 4 | **Prep Time:** 20 mins | **Cook Time:** 10 mins

Description:
Spiced lamb koftas grilled and served with a cooling tzatziki sauce, a perfect blend of flavors from the Mediterranean.

Ingredients

- 1 pound ground lamb
- 2 cloves garlic
- 1 small onion, finely chopped
- 2 tsp. ground cumin
- 1 tsp. ground coriander
- 1 tsp. paprika
- 1/2 tsp. salt
- 1/4 tsp. black pepper
- 1 cup Greek yogurt
- 1/2 cucumber,

Main Dishes

Preparation steps:

1. In a bowl, combine ground lamb, garlic, onion, cumin, coriander, paprika, salt, and pepper. Mix well and form into small sausages or patties.
2. Preheat a grill or grill pan over medium-high heat. Brush the koftas with olive oil and grill for about 4-5 minutes on each side, or until fully cooked.
3. For the tzatziki sauce, mix Greek yogurt, grated cucumber, lemon juice, and mint in a bowl. Season with salt and pepper to taste.
4. Serve the lamb koftas with tzatziki sauce on the side, garnished with additional mint or parsley if desired.

Desserts

Ingredients

- 4 large apples, such as Honeycrisp or Fuji
- 1/4 cup brown sugar
- 1 tsp. ground cinnamon
- 1/4 tsp. ground nutmeg
- 1/4 cup chopped walnuts
- 4 tsp. butter
- 1/2 cup water

BAKED APPLES WITH CINNAMON

Servings:
4

Prep Time:
10 Mins

Cook Time:
30 mins

Description:

Comforting baked apples filled with cinnamon and a hint of nutmeg, a simple yet delightful way to end a meal.

Preparation steps:

1. Preheat oven to 350°F (175°C).
2. Core the apples and place them in a baking dish
3. In a small bowl, mix together brown sugar cinnamon, nutmeg, and walnuts. Stuff this mixture into the center of each apple.
4. Top each apple with a tsp. of butter.
5. Pour water into the bottom of the baking dish around the apples.
6. Bake in the preheated oven for 30 minutes, or until the apples are tender.
7. Serve warm, possibly with a dollop of Greek yogurt or a drizzle of honey.

BERRY AND YOGURT SMOOTHIE

Servings: 2

Prep Time: 5 mins

Cook Time: 0 mins

Description:

A refreshing and nutritious smoothie made with mixed berries and Greek yogurt, perfect for a light dessert or a healthy snack.

Ingredients

- 1 cup frozen mixed berries (strawberries, blueberries, raspberries)
- 1 cup Greek yogurt
- 1 tbsp. honey
- 1/2 cup almond milk

Preparation steps:

1. Place all ingredients in a blender.
2. Blend until smooth.
3. Serve immediately, garnished with a few fresh berries or a mint leaf for a touch of elegance.

Desserts

Ingredients

- 1 cup almond butter
- 1/3 cup maple syrup
- 1 egg
- 1/4 cup unsweetened cocoa powder
- 1/2 tsp. baking soda
- 1/4 tsp. salt
- 1/2 cup dark chocolate chips (optional)

ALMOND BUTTER BROWNIES

Servings:
8

Prep Time:
10 Mins

Cook Time:
20 mins

Description:
Aa healthier take on a classic dessert that both gluten-free and delicious.

Preparation steps:

1. Preheat oven to 350°F (175°C).
2. In a bowl, mix together almond butter, maple syrup, and egg until smooth.
3. Add cocoa powder, baking soda, and salt, mixing until combined.
4. Stir in chocolate chips if using.
5. Pour the batter into a greased 8x8 inch baking pan.
6. Bake for 20 minutes or until a toothpick inserted in the center comes out clean.
7. Let cool before slicing into squares and serving.

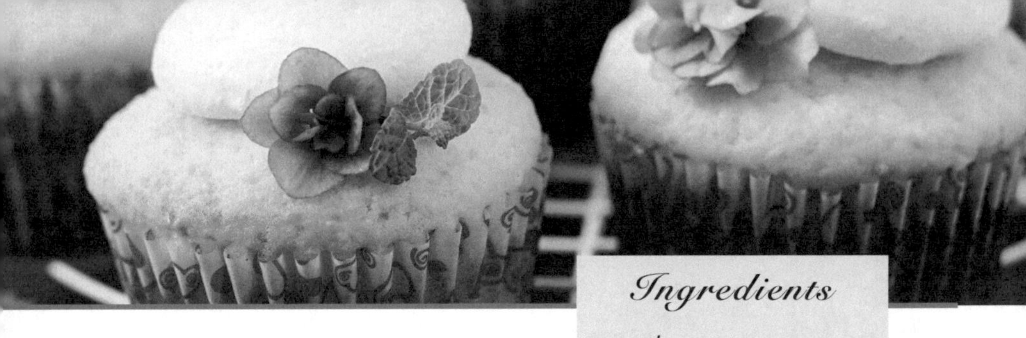

COCONUT FLOUR CUPCAKES

Servings: 12

Prep Time: 15 mins

Cook Time: 20 mins

Description:

Light and fluffy cupcakes made with coconut flour, a perfect gluten-free treat topped with a light cream cheese frosting.

Ingredients

- 3/4 cup coconut flour
- 1/2 cup butter
- 6 eggs
- 1/2 cup honey
- 1/2 tsp. vanilla extract
- 1/4 tsp. salt
- 1/2 tsp. baking powder

For frosting:

- 1/4 cup cream cheese, softened
- 1/4 cup butter
- 2 tbsp. honey
- 1/2 tsp. vanilla

Desserts

Preparation steps:

1. Preheat oven to 350°F (175°C). Line a muffin tin with cupcake liners.
2. In a large bowl, whisk together coconut flour, salt, and baking powder.
3. In another bowl, mix melted butter, eggs, honey, and vanilla extract until well combined.
4. Combine wet and dry ingredients and mix until no lumps remain.
5. Divide the batter among the muffin cups, filling each about 3/4 full.
6. Bake for 20 minutes, or until a toothpick inserted into the center comes out clean.
7. Allow cupcakes to cool completely before frosting.
8. For the frosting, beat together cream cheese,

Desserts

Ingredients

- 3 ripe mangoes, peeled and cubed
- 1/4 cup sugar (or to taste)
- Juice of 1 lime

MANGO SORBET

Servings: 4	**Prep Time:** 10 Mins	**Cook Time** 0 mins

Description:

A light and refreshing sorbet made wi[th] fresh mangoes, perfect for a sweet treat that [is] both dairy-free and low in calories.

Preparation steps:

1. Place mango cubes in a blender or food processor[.]
2. Add sugar and lime juice.
3. Blend until smooth.
4. Pour the mixture into a shallow dish and freez[e] until solid, about 4-6 hours, stirring occasionally[.]
5. Before serving, briefly process the frozen mixtur[e] again to achieve a smooth, creamy texture.
6. Serve immediately, garnished with mint leave[s] or additional mango slices if desired.

CHOCOLATE AVOCADO MOUSSE

Servings: 4
Prep Time: 10 mins
Cook Time: 0 mins

Description:
A creamy and decadent mousse made from avocados and cocoa powder, sweetened with honey, a perfect guilt-free dessert for chocolate

Ingredients

- 2 ripe avocados, peeled and pitted
- 1/4 cup cocoa powder
- 1/4 cup honey or maple syrup
- 1/2 tsp. vanilla extract
- Pinch of salt
- Optional toppings: raspberries, shredded coconut, or chopped nuts

Preparation steps:

1. In a blender or food processor, combine avocados, cocoa powder, honey, vanilla extract, and salt.
2. Blend until smooth and creamy, scraping down the sides as necessary.
3. Divide the mousse among serving dishes and refrigerate for at least 1 hour to set.
4. Garnish with optional toppings like raspberries, shredded coconut, or chopped nuts before serving.

Desserts

Ingredients

- 4 firm pears, peeled, halved, and cored
- 2 cups red wine
- 1/2 cup sugar
- 1 cinnamon stick
- 2 cloves
- 1 star anise
- Zest of 1 orange

POACHED PEARS

Servings:
4

Prep Time:
10 Mins

Cook Time:
25 mins

Description:
Elegant and aromatic poached pears, simmered in a spiced red wine reduction, perfect for a sophisticated dessert option.

Preparation steps:

1. In a saucepan large enough to hold all the pears, combine red wine, sugar, cinnamon stick, cloves, star anise, and orange zest. Bring to a simmer over medium heat.
2. Add the pear halves and reduce heat to low. Cover and simmer gently until pears are just tender, about 20-25 minutes, turning occasionally.
3. Remove pears with a slotted spoon and set aside. Increase the heat and boil the poaching liquid until reduced by half, about 10-15 minutes, to create a syrup.
4. Serve the pears with the reduced wine syrup drizzled over the top.

Desserts

RICOTTA & LEMON CHEESECAKE

Servings: 8

Prep Time: 20 mins

Cook Time: 50 mins

Description:

A lighter version of traditional cheesecake using ricotta cheese and infused with fresh lemon zest for a refreshing finish.

Ingredients

- 2 cups ricotta cheese
- 1/2 cup sugar
- 3 eggs
- Zest of 1 lemon
- 1 tsp. vanilla extract
- 1/4 cup all-purpose flour
- Pinch of salt

Preparation steps:

1. Preheat oven to 350°F (175°C).
2. In a mixing bowl, beat ricotta cheese and sugar until smooth.
3. Add eggs, one at a time, mixing well after each addition.
4. Stir in lemon zest, vanilla extract, flour, and a pinch of salt.
5. Pour the mixture into a greased 9-inch springform pan.
6. Bake in the preheated oven for 50 minutes, or until set and slightly golden on top.
7. Allow to cool completely before removing from the pan.
8. Refrigerate for at least 4 hours before serving,

Desserts

Ingredients

- 1 pie crust (store-bought or homemade)
- 8 fresh figs, quartered
- 1/4 cup honey
- 2 tbsp.s unsalted butter, melted
- 1 tsp. ground cinnamon

FIG AND HONEY TART

Servings: 8

Prep Time: 15 Mins

Cook Time 30 mins

Description:

A rustic tart filled with fresh figs and sweetned with honey, a delicious combination natural flavors and textures.

Preparation steps:

1. Preheat oven to 375°F (190°C).
2. Arrange the pie crust in a tart pan and trim th edges.
3. In a bowl, toss the fig quarters with honey melted butter, and cinnamon.
4. Arrange the fig mixture evenly over the pie crust
5. Bake in the preheated oven for about 30 minutes or until the crust is golden and the figs are tende and caramelized.
6. Let cool slightly before serving, perhaps with scoop of vanilla ice cream or a dollop of whippe cream.

CARROT CAKE & CREAM CHEESE

Servings: 12

Prep Time: 20 mins

Cook Time: 30 mins

Ingredients

- 2 cups carrots
- 1 cup whole wheat flour
- 1/2 cup almond flour
- 3/4 cup honey
- 1/2 cup unsweetened applesauce
- 2 eggs
- 1 tsp. vanilla
- 1 tsp. bake soda
- 1/2 tsp. salt
- 2 tsp.s cinnamon
- 1/4 tsp. ground nutmeg

For the frosting:

- 1/4 cup low-fat cream cheese, softened
- 1/4 cup Greek yogurt
- 2 tbsp.s honey
- 1/2 tsp. vanilla extract

Description:

Moist carrot cake spiced with cinnamon and nutmeg, providing a satisfying dessert without excessive sugar.

Preparation steps:

1. Preheat oven to 350°F (175°C). Grease a 9-inch round cake pan and line with parchment paper.
2. In a large bowl, combine whole wheat flour, almond flour, baking soda, salt, cinnamon, and nutmeg.
3. In another bowl, whisk together eggs, honey, applesauce, and vanilla extract. Stir in the grated carrots.
4. Add the wet ingredients to the dry ingredients, mixing until just combined. Fold in walnuts if using.
5. Pour the batter into the prepared cake pan.
6. Bake for about 30 minutes, or until a toothpick inserted into the center comes out clean.
7. Allow the cake to cool completely before frosting.
8. For the frosting, mix cream cheese, Greek yogurt, honey, and vanilla extract until smooth. Spread evenly over the top of the cooled cake.
9. Serve the cake garnished with additional walnuts or a sprinkle of cinnamon.

THANK YOU SO MUCH FOR MAKING IT THIS FAR!

I greatly appreciate the time you took to give my book a read. As a small indie publisher, it means a lot and I hope I am making a difference in your cooking journey.

If you have 60 seconds, hearing your honest feedback on Amazon would mean the world to me.

It does wonders for the book, and I love hearing about your experience with it!

To leave your feedback:

1. Open your camera app
2. Point your mobile device at the QR code below
3. The review page will appear in your web browser

60-DAY MEAL PLAN

The meal plan is structured around a daily intake of approximately 1200 calories, divided into three main meals and two snacks. Here's a breakdown of what your daily eating schedule might look like:

Breakfast: Start your day with a nourishing breakfast that contains around 300 calories. This meal should include protein and fiber to keep you full and energized until your mid-morning snack.

Morning Snack: A light snack of about 100 calories. This snack is designed to help maintain your energy levels and prevent overeating at lunch.

Lunch: A substantial meal providing roughly 300 calories, focusing on lean protein and vegetables to satisfy your midday nutritional needs.

Afternoon Snack: Another small snack around 100 calories to help bridge the gap between lunch and dinner.

Dinner: The most substantial meal of the day with around 400 calories. Dinner should be balanced with a good portion of protein, vegetables, and a minimal amount of healthy fats.

Tips for Success

Accurate Portion Sizes: Use measuring cups, spoons, and a kitchen scale to ensure portion sizes are accurate. This accuracy is crucial for keeping within the calorie limits specified in the meal plan.

Preparation Is Key: Prepare meals in advance whenever possible. Meal prepping helps you stick to your diet plan and avoid the temptation of opting for less healthy options when you're hungry.

Stay Hydrated: Drink plenty of water throughout the day. Sometimes, thirst is confused with hunger. Keeping hydrated can help manage hunger and aid in weight loss.

Customize to Your Taste: Feel free to swap out certain ingredients based on your dietary restrictions or preferences. However, ensure to keep the calorie count approximately the same to stay within the meal plan guidelines.

Monitor Your Progress: Keep a food diary or use a mobile app to track your meals and calories. Tracking what you eat can be an effective way to ensure you're following the meal plan correctly.

Listen to Your Body: Pay attention to how your body responds to the diet. If you feel consistently sluggish or hungry, you may need to adjust the meal timings or portion sizes slightly. Always consult with a healthcare provider

Adjusting the Plan

Not everyone's body reacts the same way to a specific diet plan. Here are a few adjustments you might consider:

Adding Variety: To prevent dietary boredom, rotate different recipes within the same calorie range. Variety can help you stay motivated and committed to your diet plan.

Incorporating Exercise: If you are able to exercise, you might need slightly more calories to compensate for the energy expended. Consult with a healthcare professional about adjusting your calorie intake when incorporating exercise into your routine.

Your Plan

If you want to print your plan, follow the instructions belo. Otherwise move to the next page

1. Open your camera app

2. Point your mobile device at the QR code below

3. Download and Print the plan

DAY	BREAKFAST (CALORIES)	MORNING SNACK (CALORIES)	LUNCH (CALORIES)	AFTERNOON SNACK (CALORIES)	DINNER (CALORIES)
1	Egg White Spinach Omelet (200)	Cucumber and Hummus Bites (100)	Grilled Chicken with Quinoa (300)	Pear and Walnut Salad (100)	Baked Salmon with Asparagus (400)
2	Greek Yogurt and Berry Parfait (250)	Spicy Roasted Chickpeas (100)	Vegetarian Stuffed Peppers (300)	Zucchini Chips (100)	Turkey Meatballs in Tomato Sauce (350)
3	Low-Carb Pancakes (200)	Kale and Apple Salad (100)	Thai Green Curry with Chicken (300)	Edamame with Sea Salt (100)	Vegan Mushroom Risotto (400)
4	Turkey and Spinach Scramble (250)	Stuffed Cherry Tomatoes (100)	Lemon Herb Tilapia with Beans (300)	Roasted Red Pepper Hummus (100)	Shrimp and Asparagus Stir-Fry (350)
5	Almond and Flaxseed Porridge (250)	Avocado Shrimp Ceviche (150)	Beef Stir-Fry with vegetables (300)	Beetroot and Goat Cheese Salad (100)	Moroccan Chicken with Couscous (350)
6	Chia Pudding with Coconut & Mango (250)	Stuffed Cherry Tomatoes (100)	Ratatouille with Baked Polenta (300)	Kale and Apple Salad (100)	Grilled Tofu Steaks with Avocado (350)
7	Mushroom and Herb Steel-Cut Oats (250)	Roasted Red Pepper Hummus (100)	Herb-Crusted Rack of Lamb (300)	Edamame with Sea Salt (100)	Cod en Papillote with Vegetables (300)
8	Zucchini and Bell Pepper Frittata (300)	Pear and Walnut Salad (100)	Lemon Herb Tilapia with Beans (300)	Beetroot and Goat Cheese Salad (100)	Lamb Koftas with Tzatziki Sauce (400)
9	Cinnamon Apple Yogurt Bowl (250)	Spicy Roasted Chickpeas (100)	Thai Green Curry with Chicken (300)	Cucumber and Hummus Bites (100)	Beef and Broccoli Stir-Fry (350)
10	Blueberry Oatmeal Bars (250)	Avocado Shrimp Ceviche (150)	Grilled Vegetable Platter (250)	Zucchini Chips (100)	Moroccan Chicken with Couscous (350)
11	Avocado Toast with Poached Egg (300)	Stuffed Cherry Tomatoes (100)	Grilled Chicken with Quinoa (300)	Spicy Roasted Chickpeas (100)	Baked Salmon with Asparagus (400)
12	Kale and Egg Breakfast Saute (300)	Cucumber and Hummus Bites (100)	Vegetarian Stuffed Peppers (300)	Pear and Walnut Salad (100)	Turkey Meatballs in Tomato Sauce (350)
13	Peanut Butter Banana Smoothie (300)	Kale and Apple Salad (100)	Thai Green Curry with Chicken (300)	Edamame with Sea Salt (100)	Vegan Mushroom Risotto (400)
14	Cottage Cheese and Pineapple Bowl (250)	Roasted Red Pepper Hummus (100)	Lemon Herb Tilapia with Beans (300)	Beetroot and Goat Cheese Salad (100)	Shrimp and Asparagus Stir-Fry (350)
15	Spinach and Quinoa Breakfast Bowls (300)	Avocado Shrimp Ceviche (150)	Beef Stir-Fry with vegetables (300)	Zucchini Chips (100)	Moroccan Chicken with Couscous (350)

DAY	BREAKFAST (CALORIES)	MORNING SNACK (CALORIES)	LUNCH (CALORIES)	AFTERNOON SNACK (CALORIES)	DINNER (CALORIES)
16	Greek Yogurt and Berry Parfait (250)	Zucchini Chips (100)	Grilled Vegetable Platter (300)	Stuffed Cherry Tomatoes (100)	Glazed Pork Tenderloin (350)
17	Low-Carb Pancakes (200)	Roasted Red Pepper Hummus (100)	Herb-Crusted Rack of Lamb (350)	Pear and Walnut Salad (100)	Scallops with Lemon Butter Sauce (350)
18	Turkey Bacon and Avocado Wrap (300)	Spicy Roasted Chickpeas (100)	Beef and Broccoli Stir-Fry (300)	Cucumber and Hummus Bites (100)	Cod en Papillote with Vegetables (300)
19	Berry Smoothie Bowl (250)	Edamame with Sea Salt (100)	Ratatouille with Baked Polenta (300)	Kale and Apple Salad (100)	Grilled Tofu Steaks with Avocado (350)
20	Spinach and Feta Breakfast Wrap (300)	Avocado Shrimp Ceviche (150)	Lemon Herb Tilapia with Beans (300)	Beetroot and Goat Cheese Salad (100)	Lamb Koftas with Tzatziki Sauce (350)
21	Almond and Flaxseed Porridge (250)	Stuffed Cherry Tomatoes (100)	Vegetarian Stuffed Peppers (300)	Zucchini Chips (100)	Thai Green Curry with Chicken (350)
22	Low-Carb Breakfast Casserole (300)	Kale and Apple Salad (100)	Beef Stir-Fry with Vegetables (300)	Edamame with Sea Salt (100)	Vegan Mushroom Risotto (400)
23	Mushroom and Herb Steel-Cut Oats (250)	Roasted Red Pepper Hummus (100)	Grilled Chicken with Quinoa (300)	Spicy Roasted Chickpeas (100)	Baked Salmon with Asparagus (350)
24	Zucchini and Bell Pepper Frittata (300)	Pear and Walnut Salad (100)	Lemon Herb Tilapia with Beans (300)	Beetroot and Goat Cheese Salad (100)	Moroccan Chicken with Couscous (350)
25	Cinnamon Apple Yogurt Bowl (250)	Cucumber and Hummus Bites (100)	Ratatouille with Baked Polenta (300)	Avocado Shrimp Ceviche (150)	Glazed Pork Tenderloin (350)
26	Egg White Spinach Omelet (200)	Spicy Roasted Chickpeas (100)	Grilled Tofu Steaks with Avocado (350)	Stuffed Cherry Tomatoes (100)	Herb-Crusted Rack of Lamb (350)
27	Greek Yogurt and Berry Parfait (250)	Cucumber and Hummus Bites (100)	Thai Green Curry with Chicken (300)	Kale and Apple Salad (100)	Shrimp and Asparagus Stir-Fry (350)
28	Low-Carb Pancakes (200)	Roasted Red Pepper Hummus (100)	Lemon Herb Tilapia with Beans (300)	Pear and Walnut Salad (100)	Beef and Broccoli Stir-Fry (350)
29	Turkey and Spinach Scramble (250)	Edamame with Sea Salt (100)	Vegan Mushroom Risotto (300)	Zucchini Chips (100)	Cod en Papillote with Vegetables (350)
30	Almond and Flaxseed Porridge (250)	Avocado Shrimp Ceviche (150)	Ratatouille with Baked Polenta (300)	Beetroot and Goat Cheese Salad (100)	Glazed Pork Tenderloin (350)

DAY	BREAKFAST (CALORIES)	MORNING SNACK (CALORIES)	LUNCH (CALORIES)	AFTERNOON SNACK (CALORIES)	DINNER (CALORIES)
31	Spinach and Feta Breakfast Wrap (300)	Stuffed Cherry Tomatoes (100)	Grilled Vegetable Platter (300)	Spicy Roasted Chickpeas (100)	Moroccan Chicken with Couscous (350)
32	Chia Pudding with Coconut & Mango (250)	Roasted Red Pepper Hummus (100)	Beef Stir-Fry with Vegetables (300)	Edamame with Sea Salt (100)	Vegan Mushroom Risotto (350)
33	Mushroom and Herb Steel-Cut Oats (250)	Kale and Apple Salad (100)	Lemon Herb Tilapia with Beans (300)	Cucumber and Hummus Bites (100)	Baked Salmon with Asparagus (350)
34	Zucchini and Bell Pepper Frittata (300)	Pear and Walnut Salad (100)	Ratatouille with Baked Polenta (300)	Beetroot and Goat Cheese Salad (100)	Glazed Pork Tenderloin (350)
35	Cinnamon Apple Yogurt Bowl (250)	Avocado Shrimp Ceviche (150)	Thai Green Curry with Chicken (300)	Zucchini Chips (100)	Shrimp and Asparagus Stir-Fry (350)
36	Blueberry Oatmeal Bars (250)	Spicy Roasted Chickpeas (100)	Grilled Chicken with Quinoa (300)	Stuffed Cherry Tomatoes (100)	Beef and Broccoli Stir-Fry (350)
37	Avocado Toast with Poached Egg (300)	Cucumber and Hummus Bites (100)	Vegetarian Stuffed Peppers (300)	Kale and Apple Salad (100)	Herb-Crusted Rack of Lamb (350)
38	Kale and Egg Breakfast Saute (300)	Roasted Red Pepper Hummus (100)	Lemon Herb Tilapia with Beans (300)	Pear and Walnut Salad (100)	Cod en Papillote with Vegetables (350)
39	Peanut Butter Banana Smoothie (300)	Edamame with Sea Salt (100)	Vegan Mushroom Risotto (300)	Beetroot and Goat Cheese Salad (100)	Thai Green Curry with Chicken (350)
40	Cottage Cheese and Pineapple Bowl (250)	Avocado Shrimp Ceviche (150)	Beef Stir-Fry with Vegetables (300)	Zucchini Chips (100)	Moroccan Chicken with Couscous (350)
41	Greek Yogurt and Berry Parfait (250)	Zucchini Chips (100)	Grilled Tofu Steaks with Avocado (350)	Stuffed Cherry Tomatoes (100)	Glazed Pork Tenderloin (350)
42	Low-Carb Pancakes (200)	Roasted Red Pepper Hummus (100)	Herb-Crusted Rack of Lamb (300)	Pear and Walnut Salad (100)	Scallops with Lemon Butter Sauce (350)
43	Turkey Bacon and Avocado Wrap (300)	Spicy Roasted Chickpeas (100)	Lemon Herb Tilapia with Beans (300)	Cucumber and Hummus Bites (100)	Vegan Mushroom Risotto (350)
44	Berry Smoothie Bowl (250)	Edamame with Sea Salt (100)	Ratatouille with Baked Polenta (300)	Kale and Apple Salad (100)	Baked Salmon with Asparagus (350)
45	Spinach and Feta Breakfast Wrap (300)	Avocado Shrimp Ceviche (150)	Thai Green Curry with Chicken (300)	Beetroot and Goat Cheese Salad (100)	Moroccan Chicken with Couscous (350)

DAY	BREAKFAST (CALORIES)	MORNING SNACK (CALORIES)	LUNCH (CALORIES)	AFTERNOON SNACK (CALORIES)	DINNER (CALORIES)
46	Almond and Flaxseed Porridge (250)	Stuffed Cherry Tomatoes (100)	Grilled Vegetable Platter (300)	Spicy Roasted Chickpeas (100)	Herb-Crusted Rack of Lamb (350)
47	Low-Carb Breakfast Casserole (300)	Kale and Apple Salad (100)	Beef Stir-Fry with Vegetables (300)	Edamame with Sea Salt (100)	Shrimp and Asparagus Stir-Fry (350)
48	Mushroom and Herb Steel-Cut Oats (250)	Roasted Red Pepper Hummus (100)	Lemon Herb Tilapia with Beans (300)	Pear and Walnut Salad (100)	Vegan Mushroom Risotto (350)
49	Zucchini and Bell Pepper Frittata (300)	Cucumber and Hummus Bites (100)	Ratatouille with Baked Polenta (300)	Beetroot and Goat Cheese Salad (100)	Thai Green Curry with Chicken (350)
50	Cinnamon Apple Yogurt Bowl (250)	Avocado Shrimp Ceviche (150)	Grilled Chicken with Quinoa (300)	Zucchini Chips (100)	Baked Salmon with Asparagus (350)
51	Blueberry Oatmeal Bars (250)	Spicy Roasted Chickpeas (100)	Vegetarian Stuffed Peppers (300)	Stuffed Cherry Tomatoes (100)	Glazed Pork Tenderloin (350)
52	Avocado Toast with Poached Egg (300)	Cucumber and Hummus Bites (100)	Thai Green Curry with Chicken (300)	Kale and Apple Salad (100)	Cod en Papillote with Vegetables (350)
53	Kale and Egg Breakfast Saute (300)	Roasted Red Pepper Hummus (100)	Beef and Broccoli Stir-Fry (300)	Pear and Walnut Salad (100)	Moroccan Chicken with Couscous (350)
54	Peanut Butter Banana Smoothie (300)	Edamame with Sea Salt (100)	Lemon Herb Tilapia with Beans (300)	Beetroot and Goat Cheese Salad (100)	Shrimp and Asparagus Stir-Fry (350)
55	Cottage Cheese and Pineapple Bowl (250)	Avocado Shrimp Ceviche (150)	Ratatouille with Baked Polenta (300)	Zucchini Chips (100)	Herb-Crusted Rack of Lamb (350)
56	Spinach and Quinoa Breakfast Bowls (300)	Spicy Roasted Chickpeas (100)	Grilled Tofu Steaks with Avocado (350)	Stuffed Cherry Tomatoes (100)	Thai Green Curry with Chicken (350)
57	Greek Yogurt and Berry Parfait (250)	Zucchini Chips (100)	Vegan Mushroom Risotto (300)	Edamame with Sea Salt (100)	Beef Stir-Fry with Vegetables (350)
58	Low-Carb Pancakes (200)	Roasted Red Pepper Hummus (100)	Lemon Herb Tilapia with Beans (300)	Pear and Walnut Salad (100)	Baked Salmon with Asparagus (350)
59	Turkey Bacon and Avocado Wrap (300)	Kale and Apple Salad (100)	Ratatouille with Baked Polenta (300)	Cucumber and Hummus Bites (100)	Moroccan Chicken with Couscous (350)
60	Berry Smoothie Bowl (250)	Avocado Shrimp Ceviche (150)	Grilled Chicken with Quinoa (300)	Beetroot and Goat Cheese Salad (100)	Glazed Pork Tenderloin (350)

Made in United States
Troutdale, OR
11/09/2024

24404767R00051